ORIGAMI

100 tear-off sheets • 5 different models

Illustrated by Anni Betts

Designed by Hannah Ahmed
Steps written by Lucy Bowman and illustrated by John Woodcock

Fox

Swan

Sailing boat

Frog

Butterfly

About origami

Origami is the art of paper folding. The name comes from a Japanese word, but people around the world have been folding paper to make models for hundreds of years. There are instructions in this book to make five traditional models, and 100 patterned sheets to make them with. The sheets are thin so that they are easy to fold and crease.

Tips

Symbols

This means turn the paper over.

This shows you where to make a fold.

This shows you which direction to move or fold the paper.

This shows you which directions to fold and unfold the paper.

Folding tips

It's always best to fold your origami on a hard, flat surface.

Line up the corners and edges of the paper carefully when making folds.

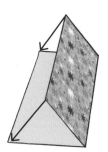

Press down on the middle of a fold first, then smooth firmly out to the sides.

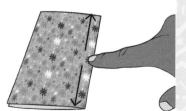

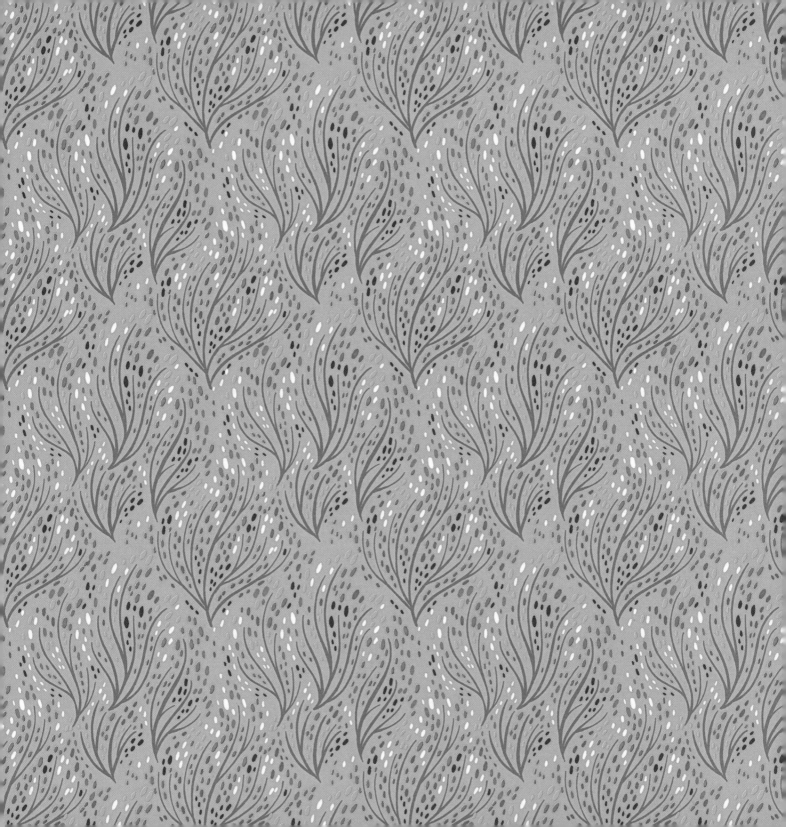

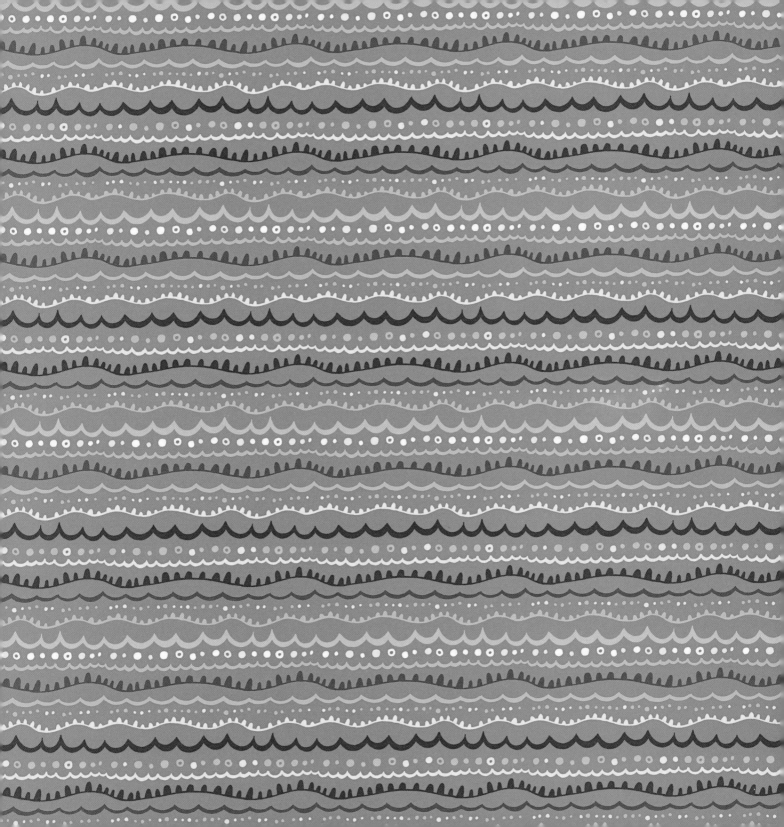

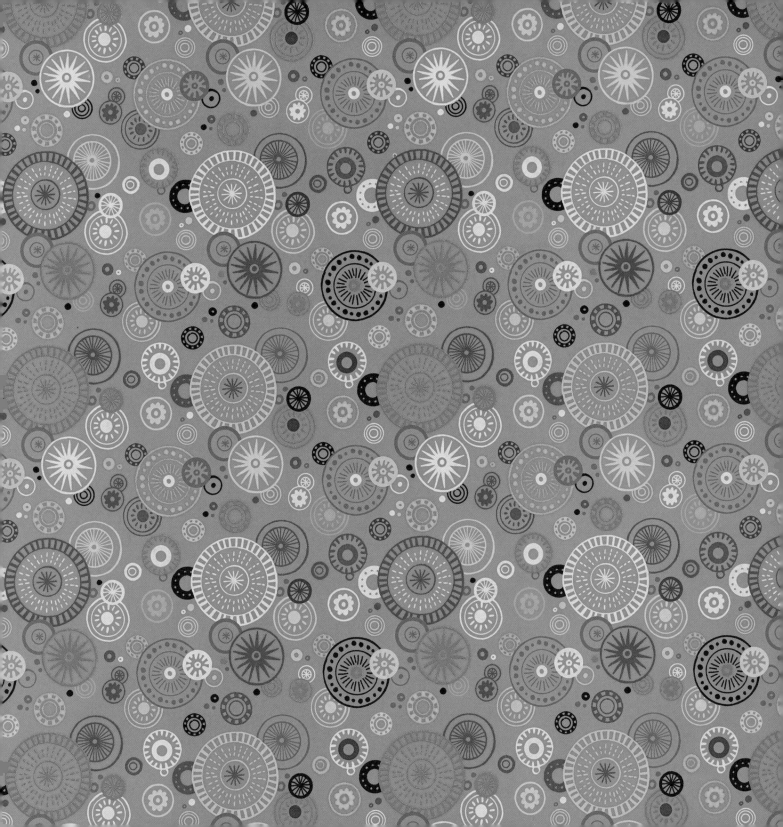

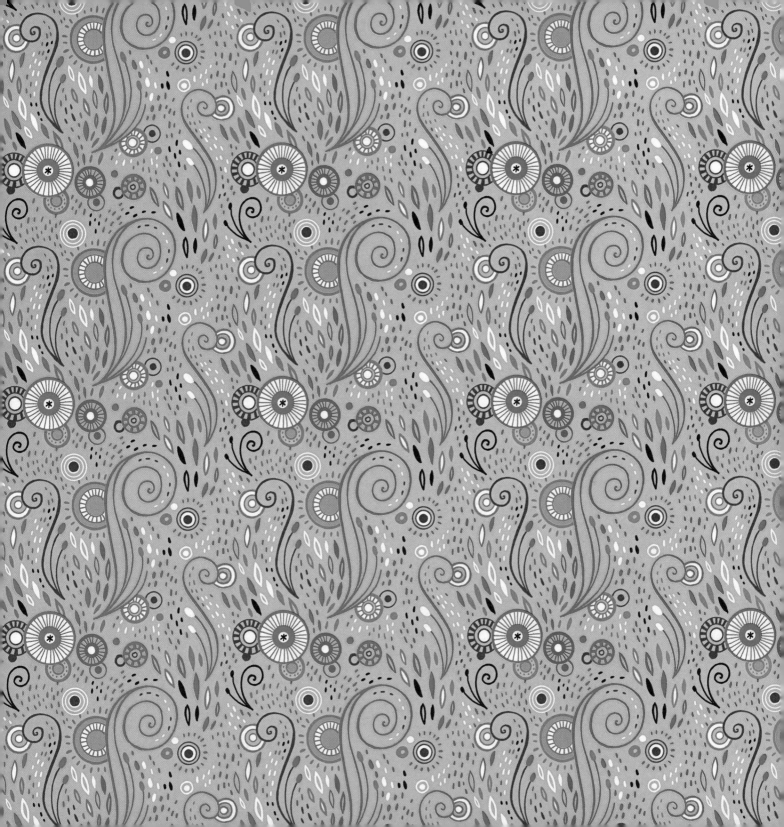

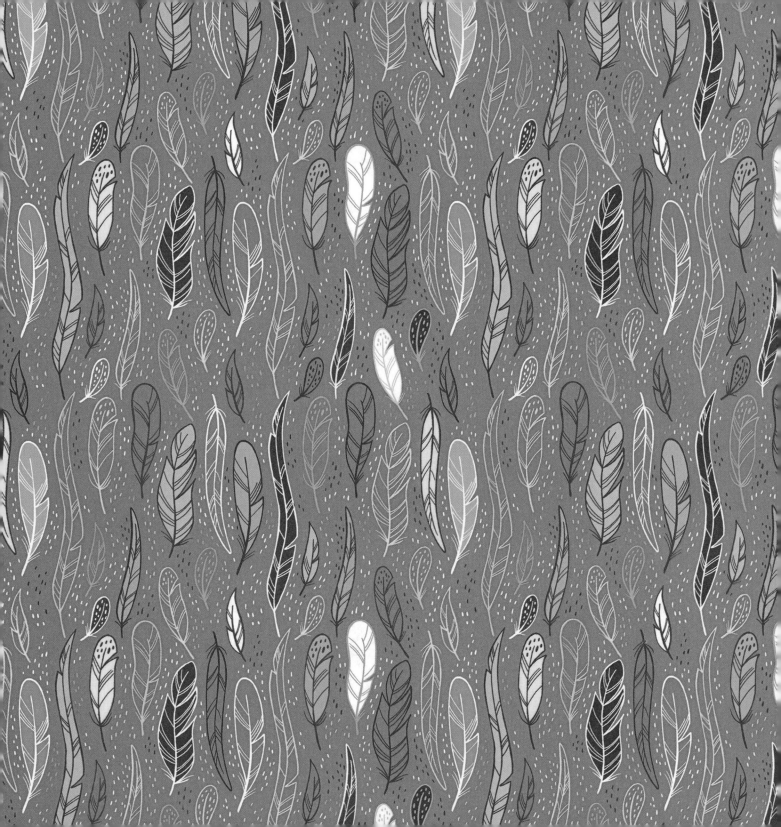

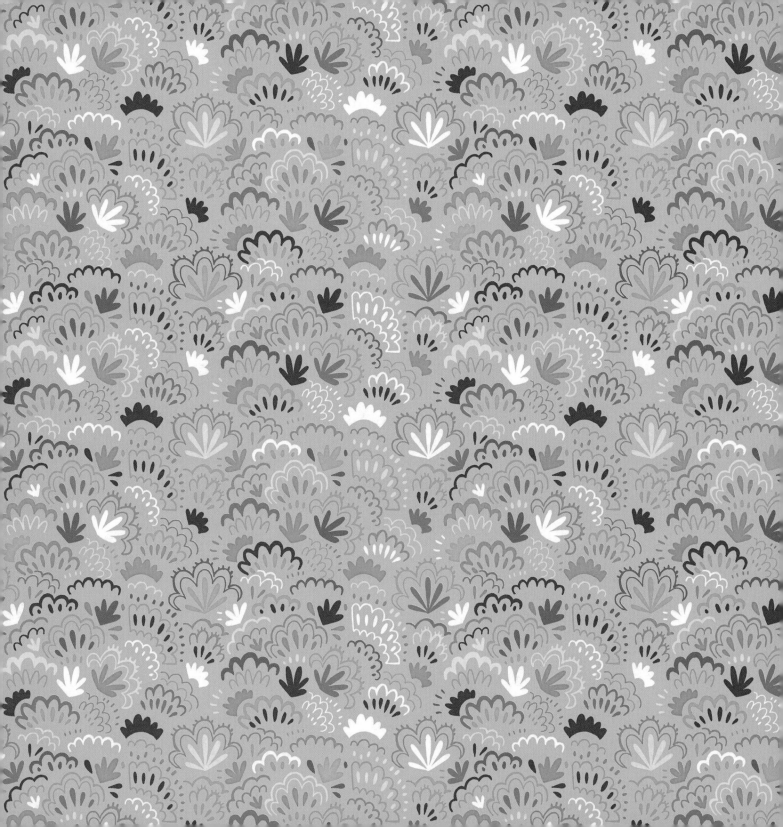

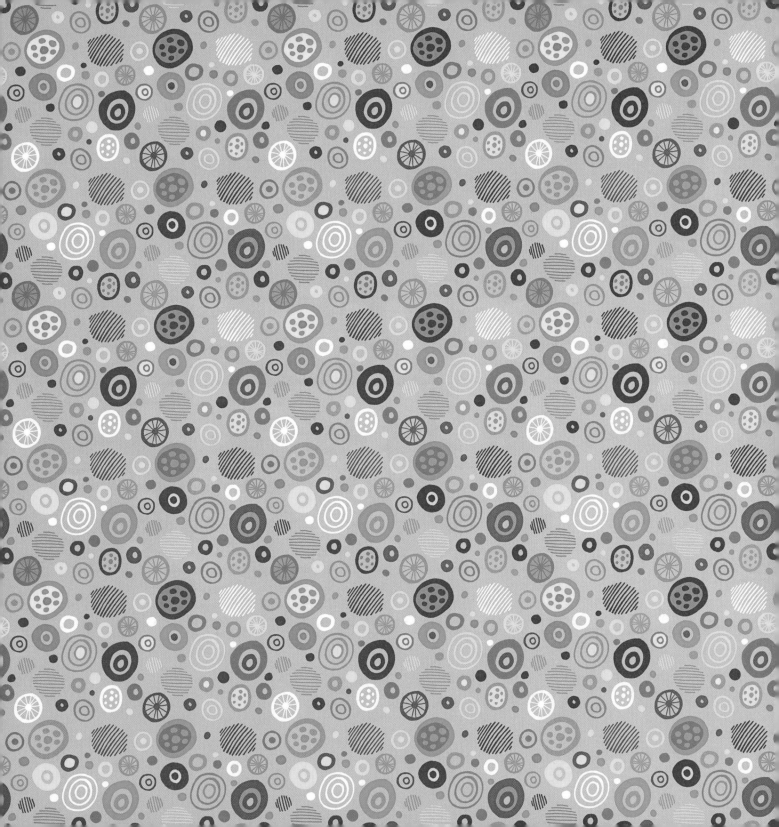

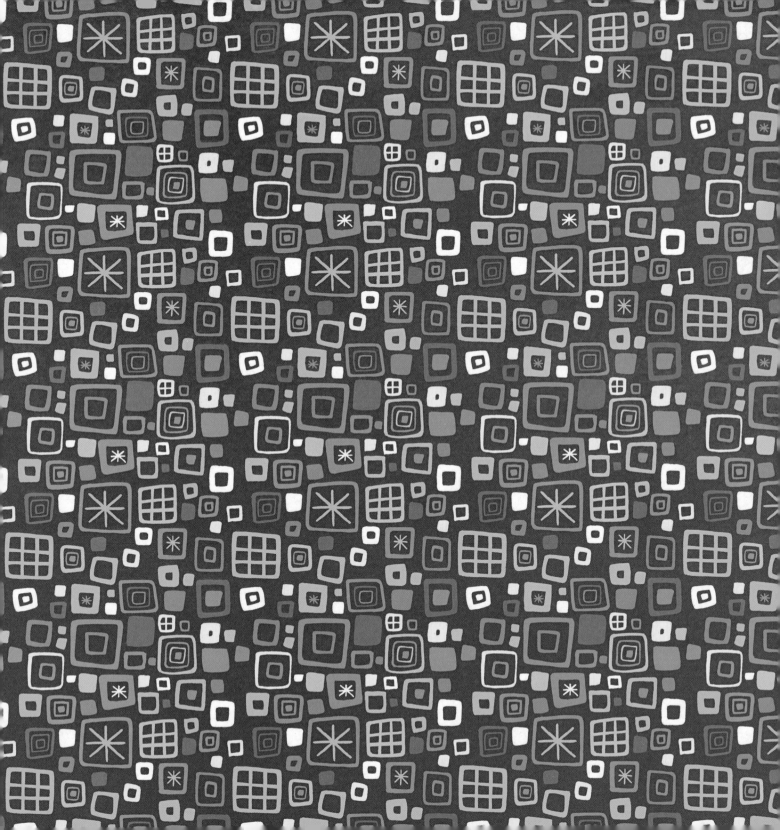

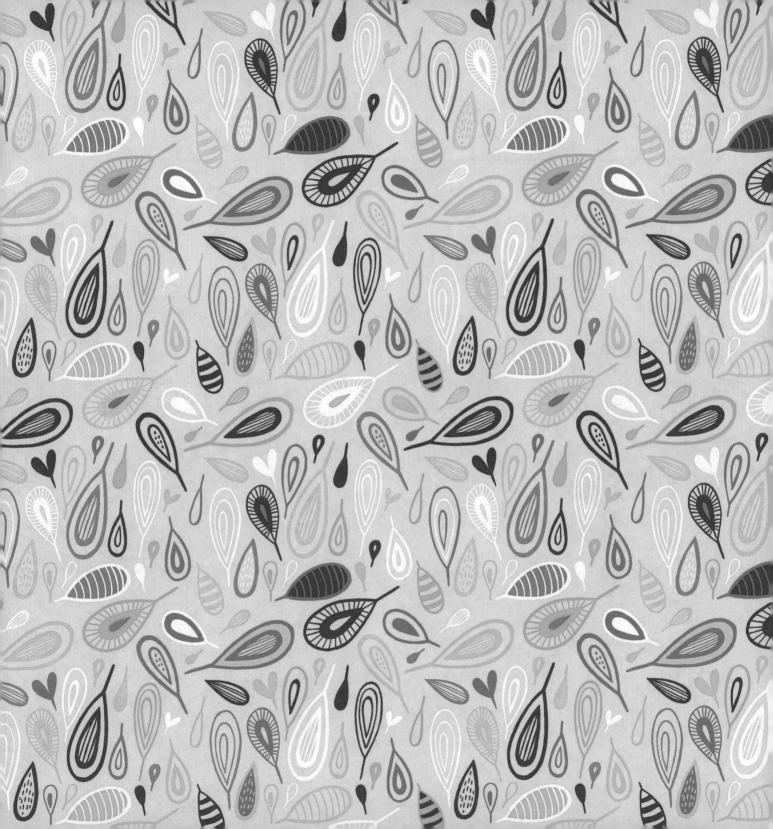

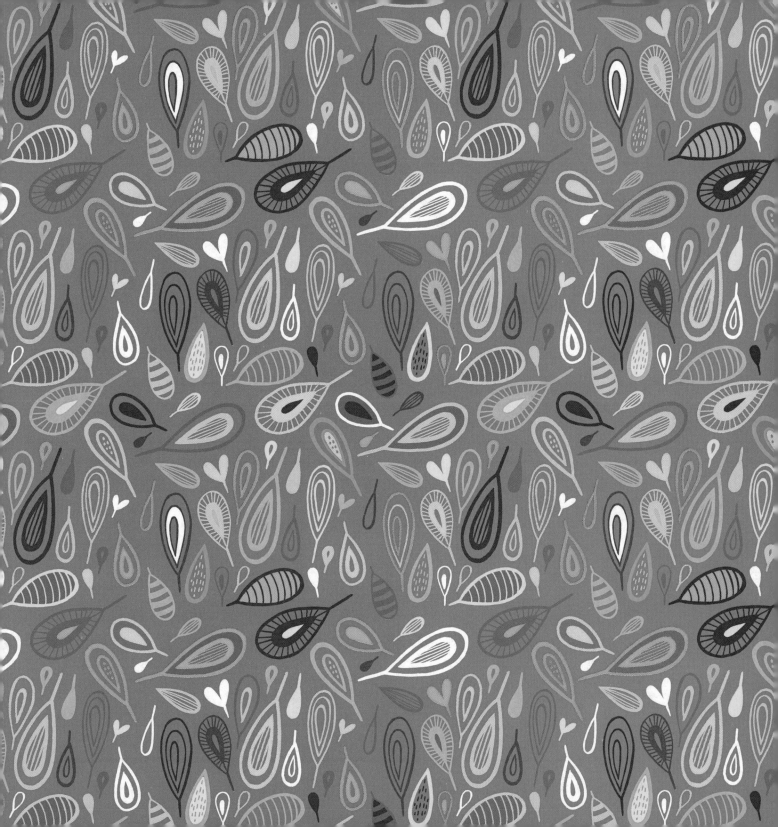

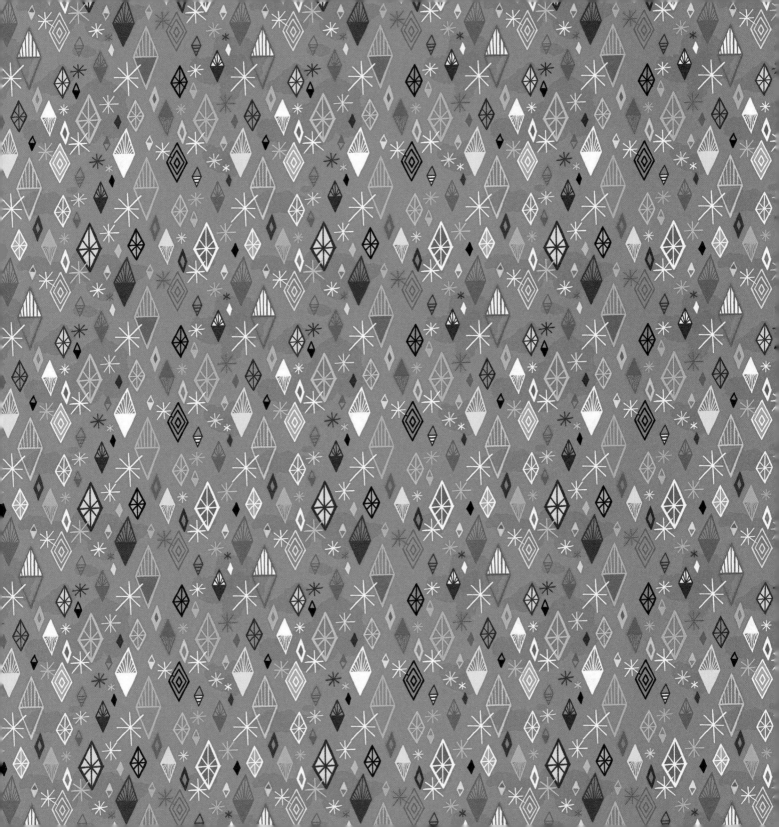

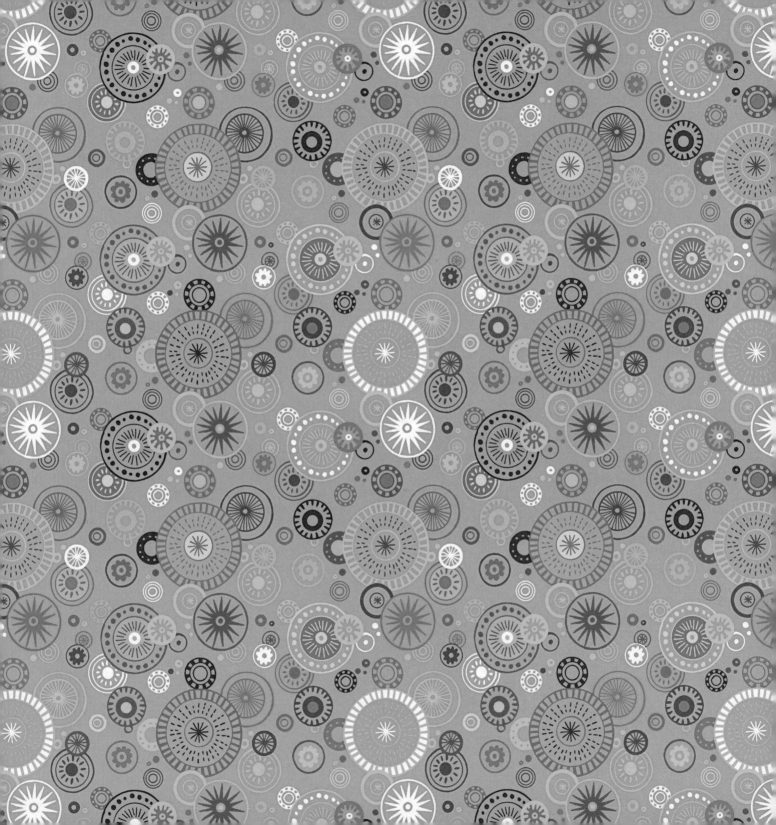

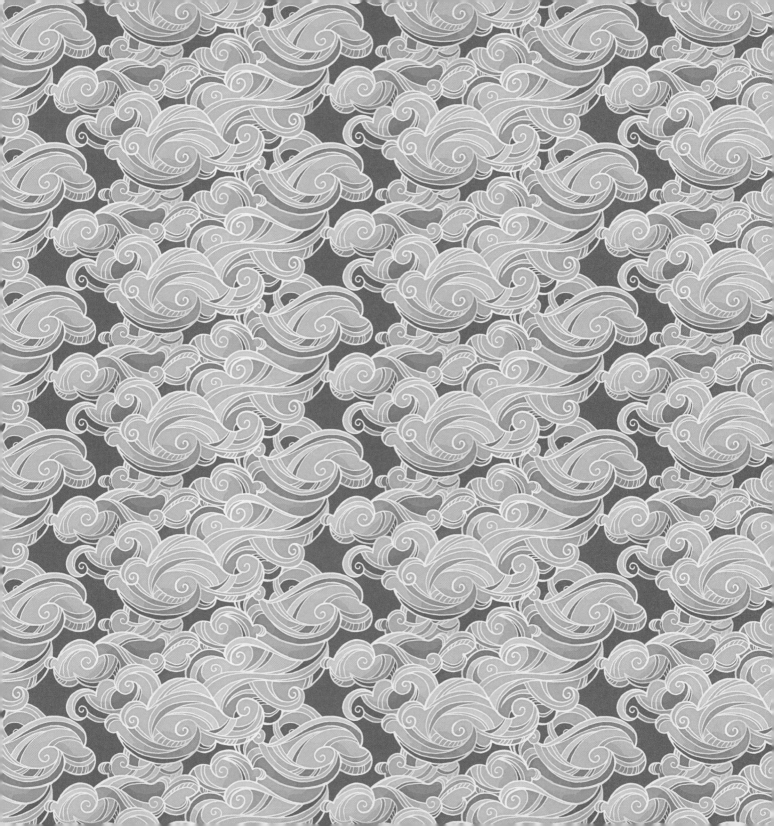

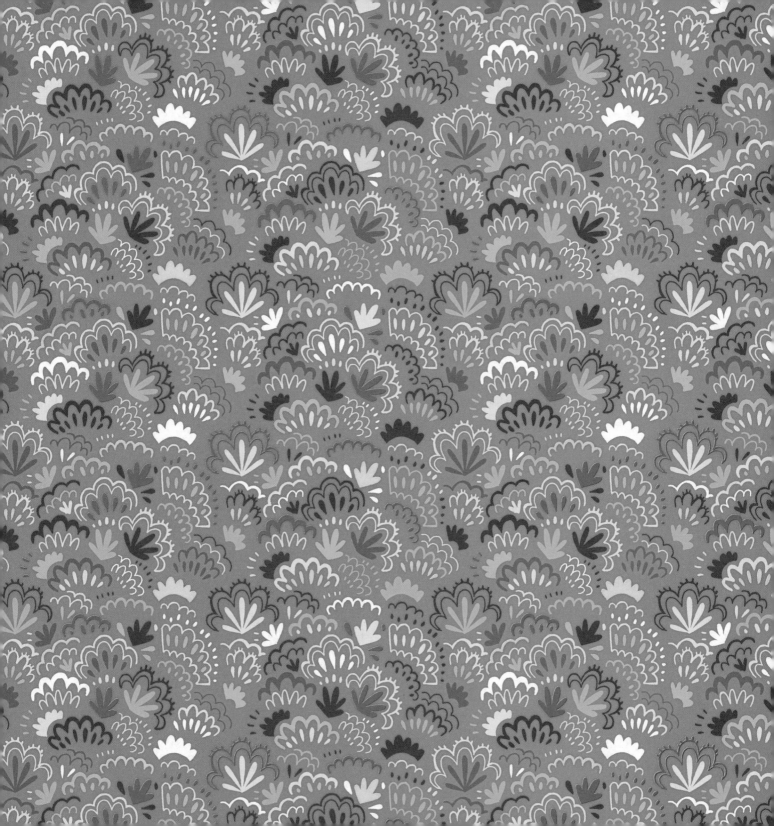

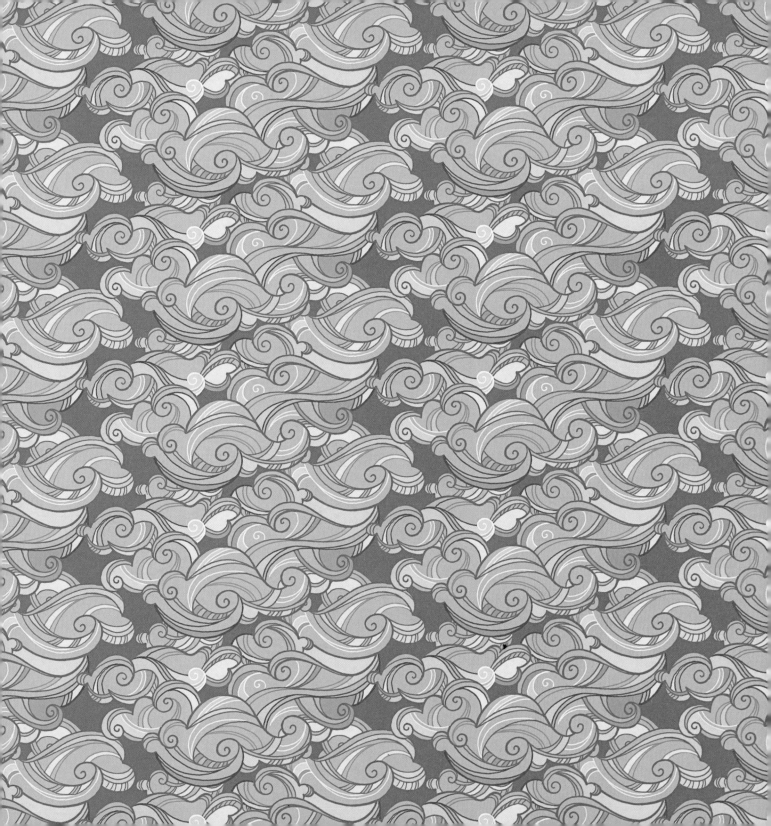

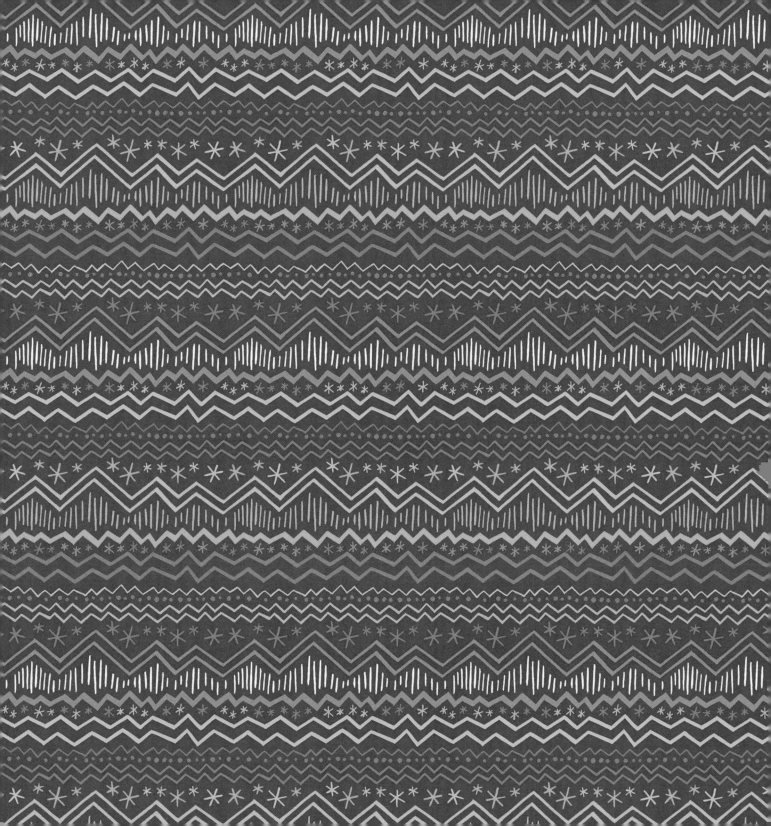

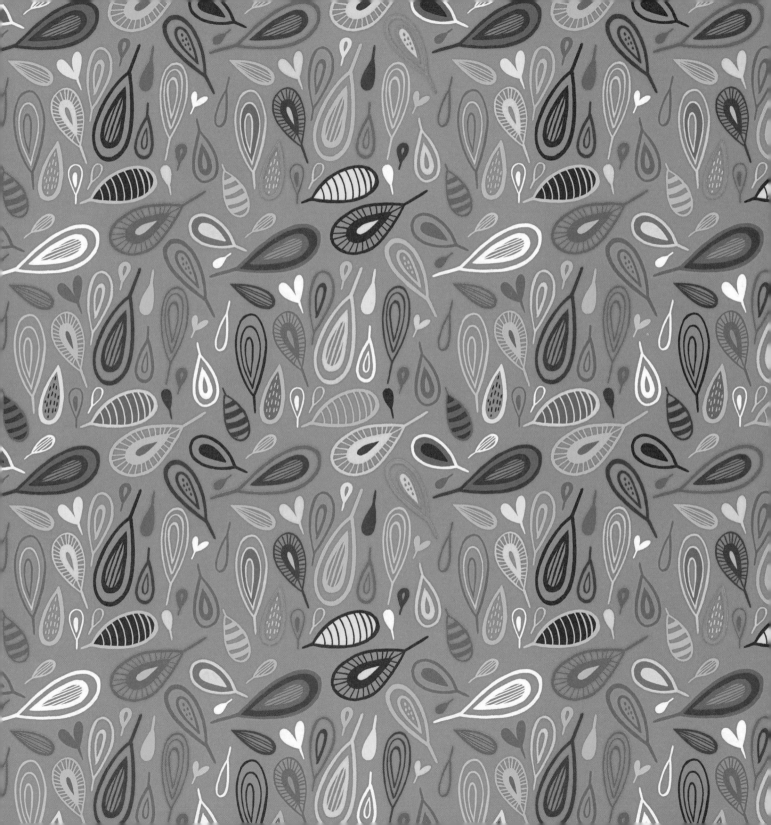